MATH+

STEP IN

Engaging math activities, games, and
fact cards **PLUS** fun math-related stories
to reinforce key math concepts!

Senior Editor: Janet Sweet
Design/Production: Rebekah Lewis
Art Director: Moonhee Pak
Managing Editor: Stacey Faulkner

Table of Contents

MATH Introduction

Understanding math is vitally important to your child's success in school and in life. The MATH series by Creative Teaching Press is expertly developed to help young children understand math concepts and ideas that relate to their world. Appealing activities and games, along with stories, fact cards, and a glossary, support math success while making math fun.

Positive attitudes about math at home—including yours as a parent—lay the foundation for math success in school. Make a point of helping your child notice math-related activities and concepts that occur in his or her daily world, such as pointing out house numbers or counting cars or noticing clothing sizes. Also encourage your child to try these activities to practice thinking mathematically:

- Sort—clothes, toys
- Measure—ingredients, sizes
- Estimate—distance, time
- Tell—where, when, and how
- Play—card and board games
- Count—stairs, grocery items
- Compare—shapes, sizes, numbers
- Pretend—to be a waiter, cashier

Helping your child experience fun, real-world math interaction at an early age will build math enjoyment, knowledge, and success throughout your child's life.

MATH Glossary

Learning math can be a challenge for young children. At a time when they are just learning to recognize and understand basic words and language skills, young learners must also figure out the symbols, concepts, and specialized vocabulary of math—all of which can seem like an entirely different language.

Specifically designed for Pre-Kindergartners and Kindergartners, this MATH Glossary of Math Words provides visual examples with clear, easy-to-understand definitions for the important math terms they must learn.

For extra support, these words also appear in red font both here and in the math-related story questions. Calling out math words in this way helps young learners understand that math is a meaningful part of everyday language and does not exist solely on math worksheets.

SYMBOLS AND CONCEPTS

¢	cent sign
even numbers	2, 4, 6, 8, 10...
odd numbers	1, 3, 5, 7, 9, 11,13...
part and whole	part whole
same and different	same different

LOCATION AND POSITION WORDS

after	16 17	17 is after 16
before	7 8	7 is before 8
between	1, 2, 3	2 is between 1 and 3
first next last	first next last	
over	The frog jumps over the log.	
under	There is water under the bridge.	

MATH⁺ Step In • Gr. PreK–K © 2011 Creative Teaching Press

COUNTING, SHAPE, AND MATH-FACT WORDS

altogether	the total of all objects or numbers in a group 3 + 2 = 5	pair	a group of 2 things that go together
compare	look at objects to learn how they are the same and different	pattern	
half		number line	1 2 3 4 5 6 7 8 9 10 Use the number line to count.
how many	asks you to count to find the answer How many legs does a spider have?	shapes	circle rectangle square triangle diamond heart oval star
less than	smaller 1 is less than 6	skip counting	counting by 2s (2, 4, 6, 8…) or by 5s (5, 10, 15, 20…) or by 10s (10, 20, 30…)
more than	bigger or larger 5 is more than 2	take away	remove from a group 5 – 3 = 2
number and number word	10 = number ten = number word	tally	1 2 3 4 5 use tally marks to count

TIME, MONEY, AND MEASUREMENT WORDS

days of the week	Sunday Monday Tuesday Wednesday Thursday Friday Saturday
height	how tall or short
length	how long or short
money	1¢ penny 5¢ nickel 10¢ dime 25¢ quarter
months of the year	January February March April May June July August September October November December
size	small medium large
temperature	how hot or cold
time of day	morning, afternoon, evening, night
weight	how heavy or light

MATH+ Step In • Gr. PreK–K © 2011 Creative Teaching Press

At the Supermarket

- Look at Lynn's list of food.

- Now look for the food in the picture below.

- Circle the food on her list to make a path to the checkout counter.

Lynn's List

2 bananas   1 bread

3 carrots   1 milk

2 tomatoes   1 lettuce

First Things First

Circle what happened first.

1

2

3

MATH+ Step In • Gr. PreK–K © 2011 Creative Teaching Press

Connect the Numbers

⚙ Connect the numbers.

⚙ Start at the number 1 and end at the number 20.

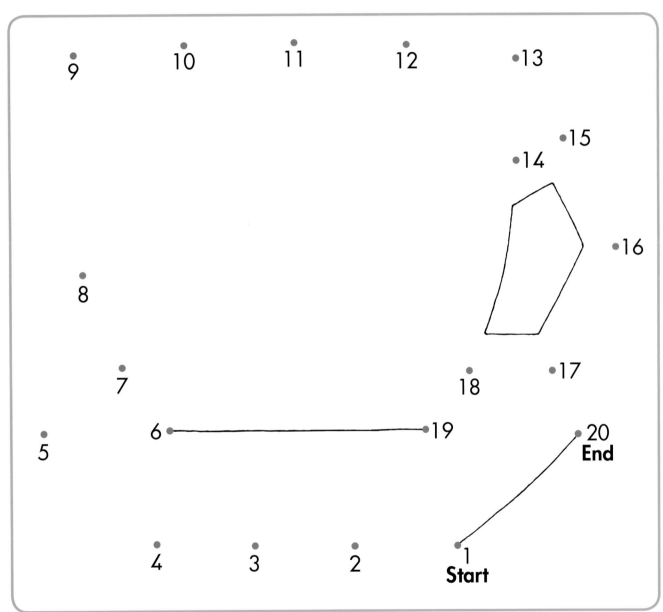

The picture is a _____ .

Things That Are Empty

✺ Circle the things that are empty.

MATH+ Step In • Gr. PreK–K © 2011 Creative Teaching Press

Number Word Fun

- Use the letters in the word **ten** to complete each word below.
- Use the picture clues to help you.

t	e	n

1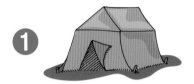

			t

2

c			

3

n		

4

	o		

5

p	l	a			

123 What's Missing?

Fill in the blanks with the missing numbers.

1 ___ 3 ___ 5 6

7 ___ ___ ___ 11 ___

___ 14 15 ___ 17 ___

___ 20 ___ 22

___ 24 ___

___ 27 ___

29 ___

Hidden Picture

✿ Follow the directions to see what is hiding.

✿ Write your answer below.

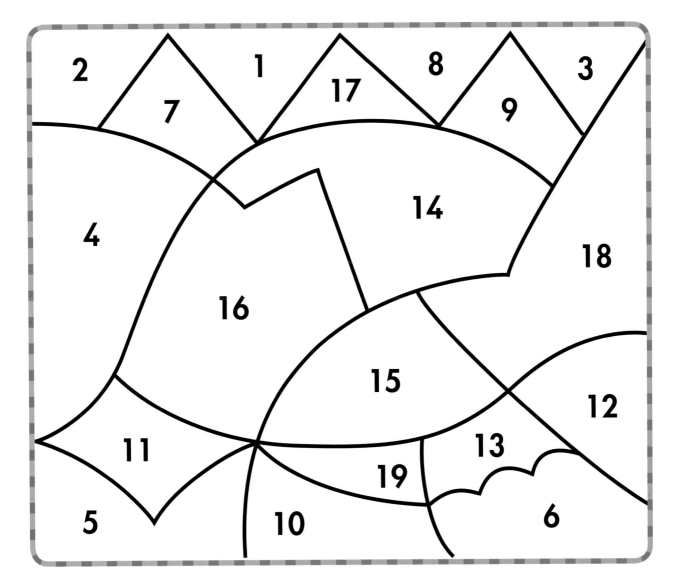

1 Color the spaces with numbers 1–13 blue.

2 Color the spaces with numbers 14–19 orange.

What did you find? _____

An Odd Snowman

❄ Use the key to color the snowman.

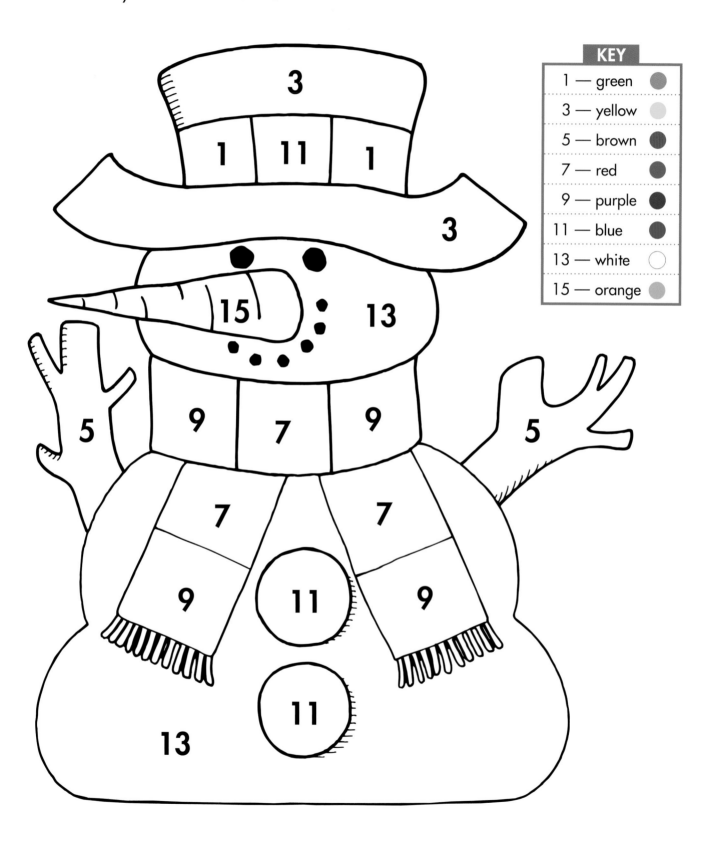

KEY

1 — green	●
3 — yellow	●
5 — brown	●
7 — red	●
9 — purple	●
11 — blue	●
13 — white	○
15 — orange	●

MATH+ Step In • Gr. PreK–K © 2011 Creative Teaching Press

Hidden Numbers

⚙ Circle the hidden numbers.

⚙ Then write how many you found.

KEY	
0	zero
3	three
5	five
8	eight
9	nine

I found _____ hidden zeros.

I found _____ hidden threes.

I found _____ hidden fives.

I found _____ hidden eights.

I found _____ hidden nines.

Go Fish 1-25

- Connect the dots.
- Color the picture.

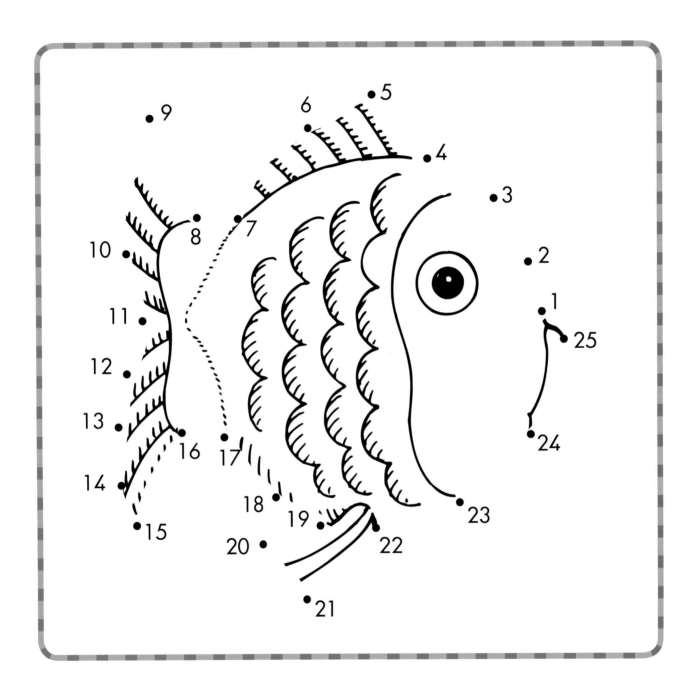

MATH+ Step In • Gr. PreK–K © 2011 Creative Teaching Press

The Beehive Maze

Circle the odd numbers to help the bee get to the hive.

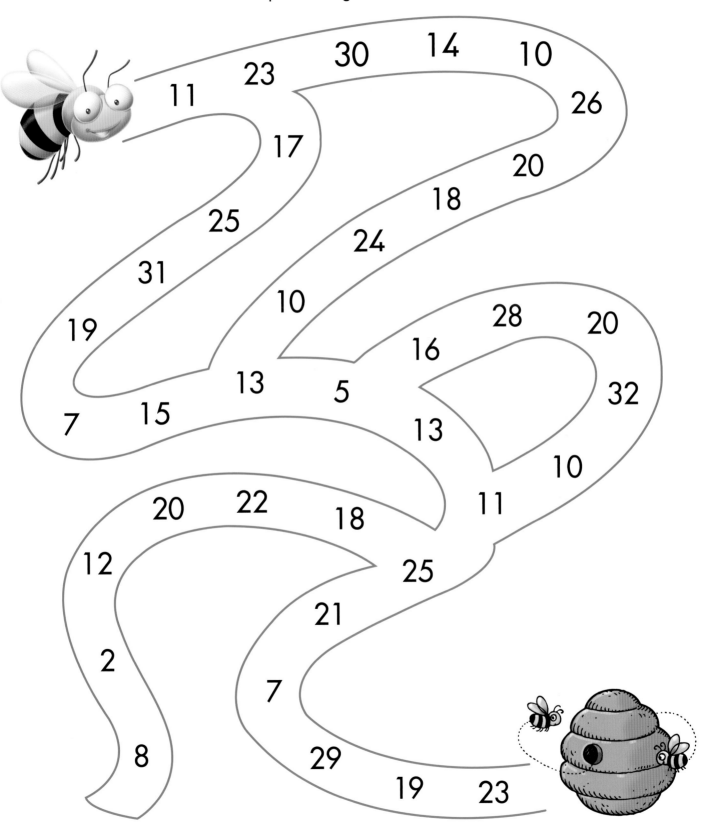

The Hidden Path

Color the triangles to help the gingerbread man find his way home.

MATH+ Step In • Gr. PreK–K © 2011 Creative Teaching Press

Dot-to-Dot Skip Counting

⚙ Connect the numbers.

⚙ What are the pictures?

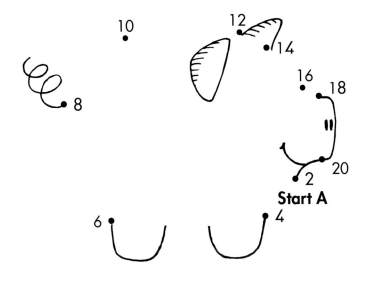

A. I counted by _____.

The picture is a _____.

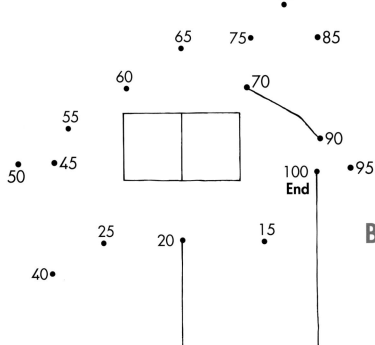

B. I counted by _____.

The picture is a _____.

Open or Closed?

- Circle the things that are open.
- Cross out the things that are closed.

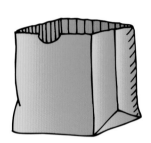

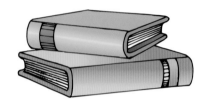

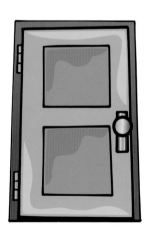

MATH+ Step In • Gr. PreK–K © 2011 Creative Teaching Press

What Comes Next?

⚙ Look at the pattern.

⚙ Circle the item that comes next.

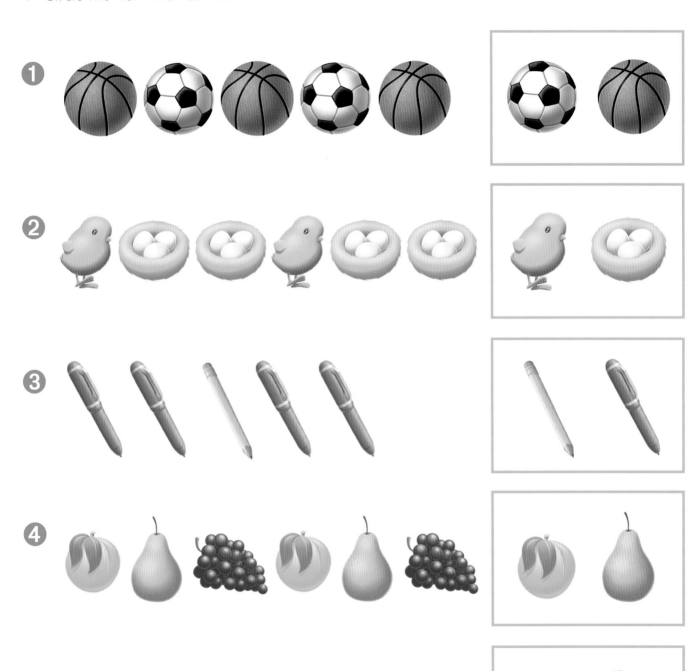

Day or Night?

- Look at the pictures below.
- Draw a line from each picture to its time of day.

day

night

MATH+ Step In • Gr. PreK–K © 2011 Creative Teaching Press

Match the Opposites

- Look at each picture.
- Draw the lines to match the opposites.

big •

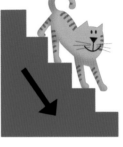

• down

happy •

• little

up •

• sad

full •

• empty

Finish the Patterns

- Look at the pattern in each row.
- Circle the picture that comes next.

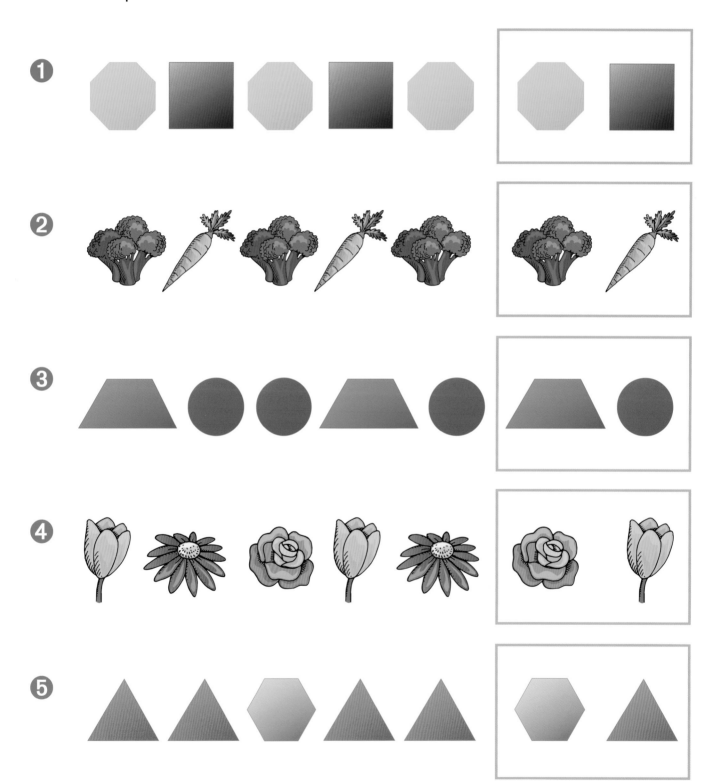

1
2
3
4
5

MATH+ Step In • Gr. PreK–K © 2011 Creative Teaching Press

Match the Shapes

✸ Draw a line to connect the shapes that are the same.

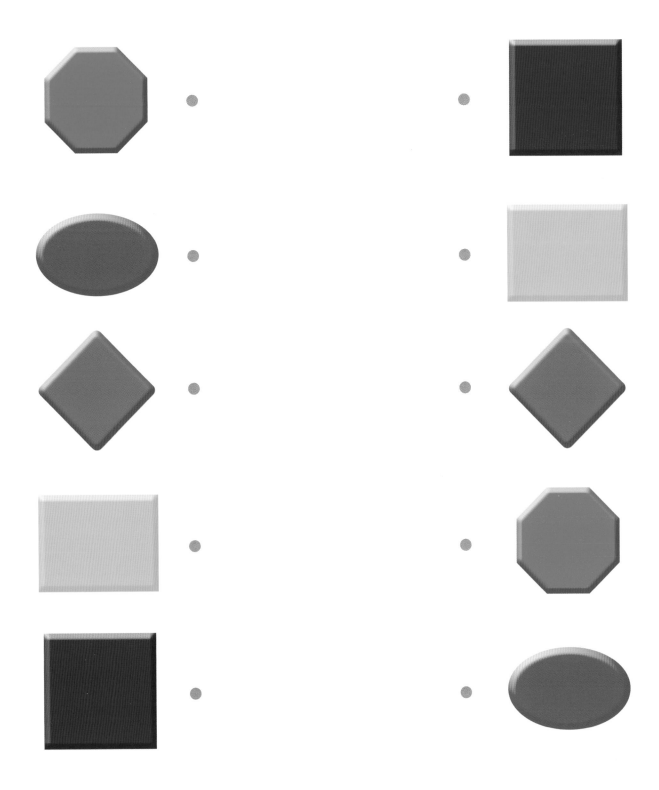

Count and Write Animals

⚙ Count the animals in the large picture.

⚙ Write the number words for how many you see.

 _____

 _____

 _____

 _____

MATH+ Step In • Gr. PreK–K © 2011 Creative Teaching Press

First, Next, Last

- Look closely at the pictures.
- Write **first**, **next**, and **last** to put them in order.

_____   _____   _____

_____   _____   _____

_____   _____   _____

MATH+ Step In • Gr. PreK–K © 2011 Creative Teaching Press

What's Different?

- Look at each group of fruit.
- Circle the one that is different.

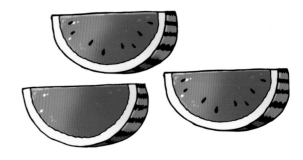

MATH⁺ Step In • Gr. PreK–K © 2011 Creative Teaching Press

Pick a Pair

Circle the pair.

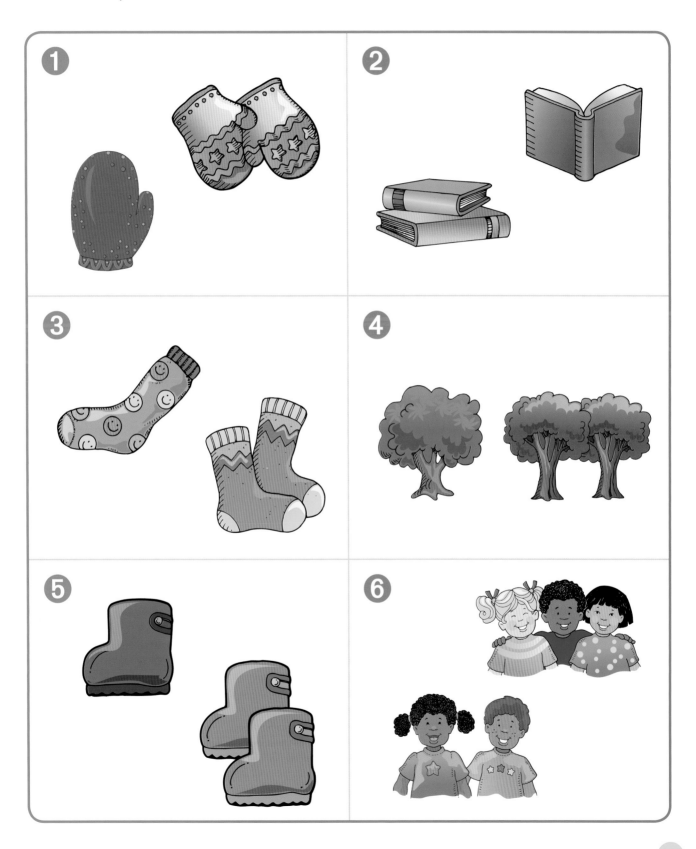

Look and Find

- Look closely.
- Find these animals in the picture.
- Circle them.

Match It!

- Look at the shadows below.
- Draw a line from each shadow to the food.

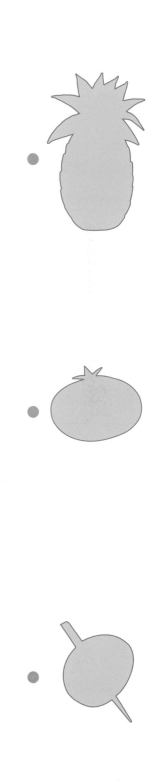

What Does Not Belong?

Circle the object that does not belong.

School

Kitchen

Repair Shop

Garden

MATH+ Step In • Gr. PreK–K © 2011 Creative Teaching Press

More or Less?

✿ Circle the object that holds more.

① ② ③ ④ ⑤ ⑥

I See Shapes

I see triangles.

✿ Look closely.

✿ How many triangles do you count?

Now I see hats.

⚙ Compare the hats to the triangles on page 35.

⚙ How are they the same?

MATH+ Step In • Gr. PreK–K © 2011 Creative Teaching Press

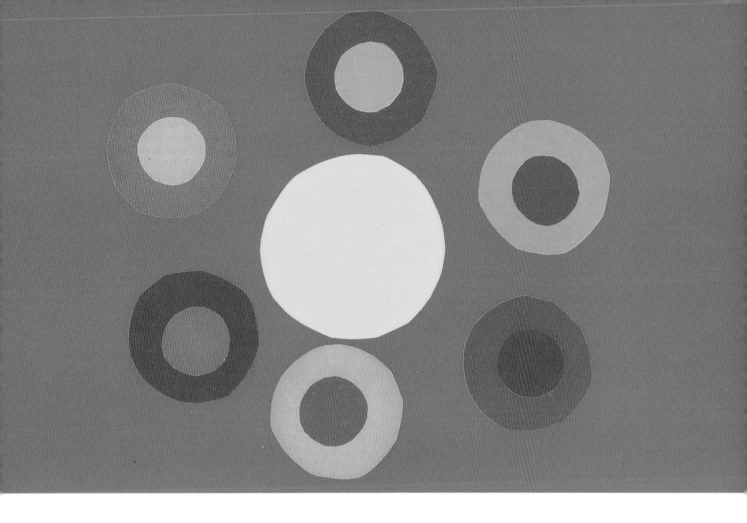

I see circles.

⚙ Look closely.

⚙ How many circles do you count?

Now I see balloons.

How many **balloons** have a **star shape**?

MATH+ Step In • Gr. PreK–K © 2011 Creative Teaching Press

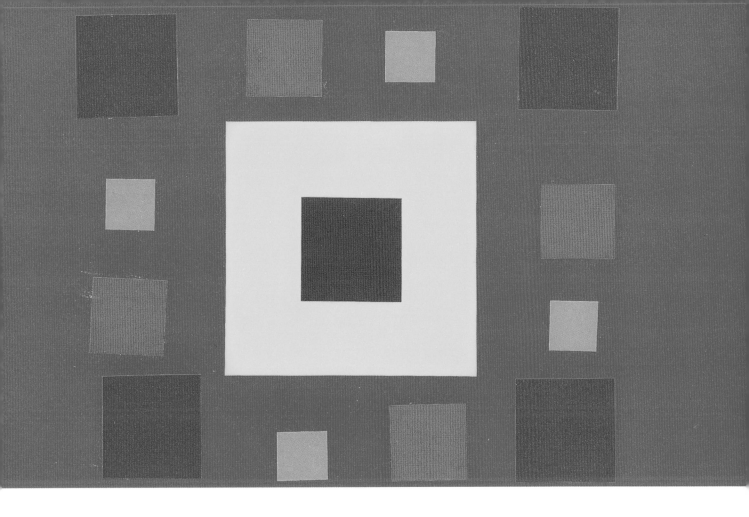

I see squares.

☼ Look closely.
☼ How many squares **do you** count?

Now I see presents.

⚜ How many presents have a heart shape?

I see rectangles.

✿ How many **yellow** rectangles do **you** count?

Now I see a cake. Happy birthday!

⚙ Name 2 shapes you see on the shirts.

MATH+ Step In • Gr. PreK–K © 2011 Creative Teaching Press

Match the Shapes

- ✿ Look at the first picture in each row.
- ✿ Color the matching shape in the row.
- ✿ Say the names of the shapes.

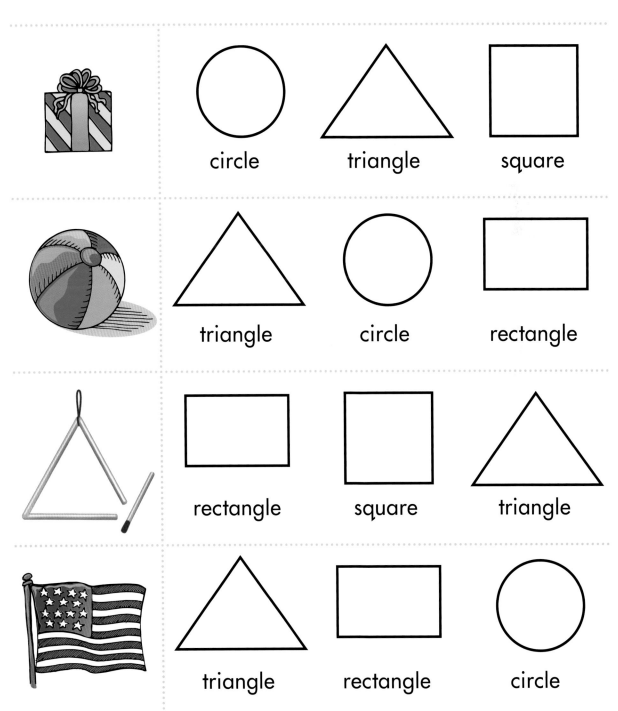

	circle	triangle	square
	triangle	circle	rectangle
	rectangle	square	triangle
	triangle	rectangle	circle

Count and Write Shapes

✪ Count the shapes on the train's engine.

✪ Write the number word for how many you see.

circle _____

triangle _____

square _____

rectangle _____

MATH⁺ Step In • Gr. PreK–K © 2011 Creative Teaching Press

Scaredy Cat Runs Away

✿ What do you see on the grass between the bear and Scaredy Cat?

Scaredy Cat ran under the fence.

✸ What is the opposite of "under"?

MATH+ Step In • Gr. PreK–K © 2011 Creative Teaching Press

The bear jumped over the fence.

✷ Is the bear running before or after
Scaredy Cat?

Scaredy Cat ran in front of the tree.

✪ What part of the tree is the birdhouse on?

MATH⁺ Step In • Gr. PreK–K © 2011 Creative Teaching Press

The bear ran behind the tree.

✿ What part of the tree is the squirrel on?

Scaredy Cat ran around the mud.
The bear ran through the mud.

✸ Why didn't they jump over the mud?

"Stop!" said the bear.
"Oh, no!" said Scaredy Cat.

✿ Is the book over or under Scaredy Cat's head?

"Here's your book!" said the bear.
"Thanks!" said Scaredy Cat.

☼ Compare **their** heights.

☼ Who is taller?

MATH+ Step In • Gr. PreK–K © 2011 Creative Teaching Press

Where Did They Go?

⚙ Trace the words.

⚙ Read to find out where Scaredy Cat and the bear went.

under

the fence

over

the fence

in front of

the tree

behind

the tree

Scaredy Cat or the Bear?

⚙ Look at the picture.

⚙ Then read the questions and circle the answers.

Who is scared?

Who is going through the mud?

Who is going around the mud?

Who is holding a book?

MATH+ Step In • Gr. PreK–K © 2011 Creative Teaching Press

☼ Name 2 pairs of things you see here.

SNIFF

I see one scary nose.

☀ What is 1 more than "one"?

I see one scary nose and two scary eyes.

☼ What is 1 more than "two"?

I see one scary nose, two scary eyes, and three scary teeth.

☼ How many more is "three" than "two"?

MATH+ Step In • Gr. PreK–K © 2011 Creative Teaching Press

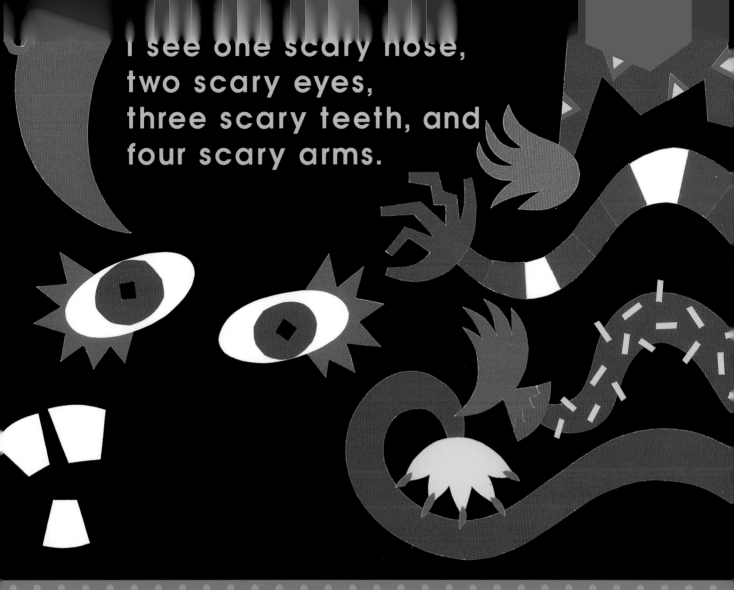

I see one scary nose,
two scary eyes,
three scary teeth, and
four scary arms.

✦ What number word will come next?

I see one scary nose,
two scary eyes, three scary teeth,
four scary arms, and
five scary legs.

What is 1 more than "five"?

MATH+ Step In • Gr. PreK–K © 2011 Creative Teaching Press

see one scary nose,
wo scary eyes,
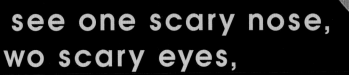

three
scary
teeth,

four scary arms,
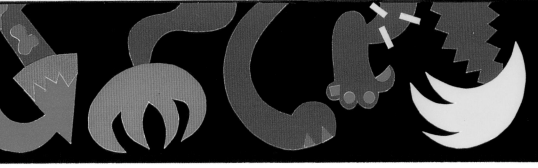

five
scary legs,
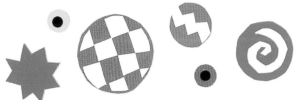

and six scary spots.

⚙ Count all the parts in this list.

⚙ How many are there altogether?

What do you see?

I see *one* scary monster!

⚙ The monster has 1 more part here that is new. What is it?

MATH+ Step In • Gr. PreK–K © 2011 Creative Teaching Press

What Do You See?

⚙ Color the spaces with **4** green.

⚙ Color the spaces with **5** blue.

⚙ Color the spaces with **6** yellow.

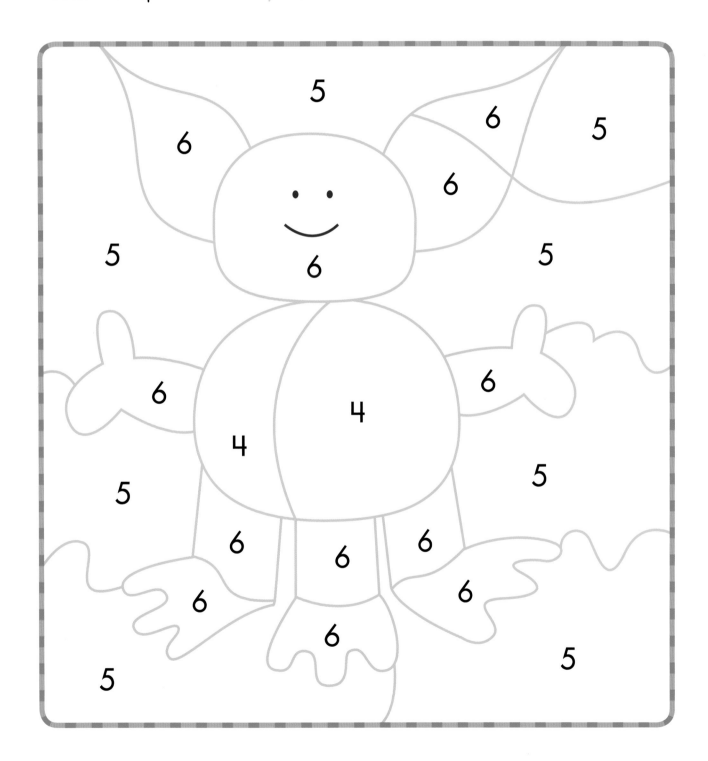

Make Your Own Monster

☼ Follow the directions.

☼ Add parts to the shapes below to make your monster.

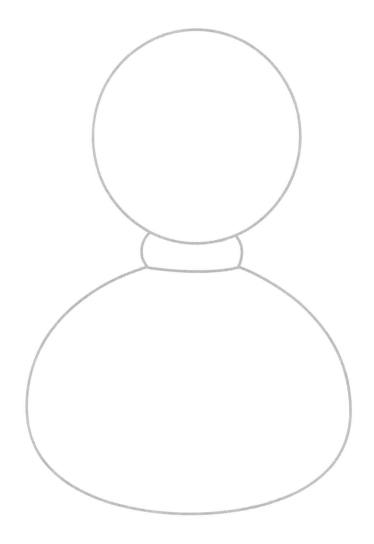

❶ Draw one scary nose.

❷ Draw two scary eyes.

❸ Draw three scary teeth.

❹ Draw four scary arms.

❺ Draw five scary legs.

❻ Draw six scary spots.

A-Counting We Will Go

✸ How are the girl and the cat the same?

Oh, a-counting we will go,
A-counting we will go.

What odd numbers do you see?

MATH+ Step In • Gr. PreK–K © 2011 Creative Teaching Press

We'll count the bugs
And put them on rugs,
And then we'll let them go!

☼ How many bugs do you count?

Oh, a-counting we will go,
A-counting we will go.

⚙ Compare this page to page 66.

⚙ What number was taken away?

MATH+ Step In • Gr. PreK–K © 2011 Creative Teaching Press

We'll count the frogs
And put them on logs,
And then we'll let them go!

⚙ How many frogs and how many logs
do you count altogether?

Oh, a-counting we will go,
A-counting we will go.

✲ What even numbers do you see here?

MATH+ Step In • Gr. PreK–K © 2011 Creative Teaching Press

**We'll count the cats
And put them on mats,
And then we'll let them go.**

✺ How many pairs of cats have the same color?

Oh, a-counting we will go,
A-counting we will go.

✿ How many more is 2 than 1?

MATH+ Step In • Gr. PreK–K © 2011 Creative Teaching Press

We'll count the foxes
And put them in boxes,
And then we'll let them go.

⚙ Look closely at the pair of foxes.
⚙ Name 2 pairs of things on their bodies.

Oh, a-counting we will go,
A-counting we will go.

☼ If you take away numbers 1–5, how many numbers are left?

MATH+ Step In • Gr. PreK–K © 2011 Creative Teaching Press

We'll count the hens
And put them in pens,
And then we'll let them go.

✺ How many hens and how many pens
do you count altogether?

Oh, a-counting we will go,
A-counting we will go.

If you take away the odd numbers,
how many numbers are left?

MATH+ Step In • Gr. PreK–K © 2011 Creative Teaching Press

We'll count the bees
And put them in trees,
And then we'll let them go.

✺ How many bees and how many trees
do you count altogether?

Oh, a-counting we will go,
A-counting we will go.

✺ Look at this page and page 79.

✺ Name the even numbers.

MATH⁺ Step In • Gr. PreK–K © 2011 Creative Teaching Press

We'll count the goats
And put them in boats,
And then we'll let them go!

⚙ Half of the goats are on each page.
How many is half?

Oh, a-counting we will go,
A-counting we will go.

We'll count the bears
And put them in chairs,
And then we'll let them go!

☼ How many bears and how many chairs
do you count altogether?

MATH+ Step In • Gr. PreK–K © 2011 Creative Teaching Press

I Know Number Words

⚙ Read the number words in the Word Box.

⚙ Write the correct word to show how many animals or people.

Word Box

one	two	three	four	five	six	seven	eight	nine

six

_____

_____

_____

_____

_____

_____

_____

_____

_____

How Many?

✿ Count and write the missing numbers.

① I see ___ foxes.

② I will make ___ wishes.

③ I see ___ cats.

④ I count ___ dishes.

⑤ Do you count ___ bears?

⑥ I see ___ sixes.

6 6 6 6 6 6

MATH+ Step In • Gr. PreK–K © 2011 Creative Teaching Press

What Goes Together?

✪ Name a **pair** of things that are **part** of the bike.

A sock and a shoe.

☼ **What do you see that** goes together **with the bat?**

MATH+ Step In • Gr. PreK–K © 2011 Creative Teaching Press

Scissors and glue.

⚙ Name 2 ways that Fox and Rabbit are the same.

Water and fish.

✿ Name 1 more thing that goes together with the fish.

MATH+ Step In • Gr. PreK–K © 2011 Creative Teaching Press

A cup and a dish.

✿ What goes together with the flower?

A bird in a tree.

✸ **What** parts go together **to make the tree?**

A friend and me.

✿ Look closely to find pairs of things.
✿ Name 2 pairs that you see.

That's what goes together!

☼ What goes together with you?

MATH+ Step In • Gr. PreK–K © 2011 Creative Teaching Press

What Goes Together?

⚙ Draw lines to match the things that go together.

What Do You Have?

⚙ Write the missing numbers.

① I have _____ eyes.

② I have _____ ears.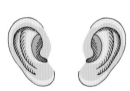

③ I have _____ little nose.

④ I have _____ hands.

⑤ I have _____ feet.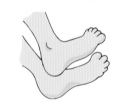

⑥ I have _____ little toes.

Tickle!
Tickle!

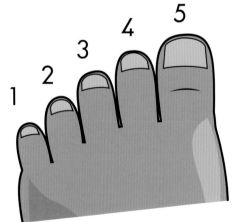
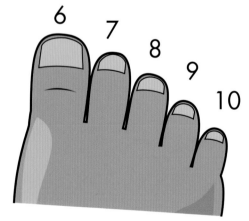

The Moving Frog

1 Cut out the squares. Put them in order from lowest number to highest number.

2 Staple the squares together on the left.

3 Flip quickly through the pictures and watch what happens!

MATERIALS
✓ scissors
✓ stapler

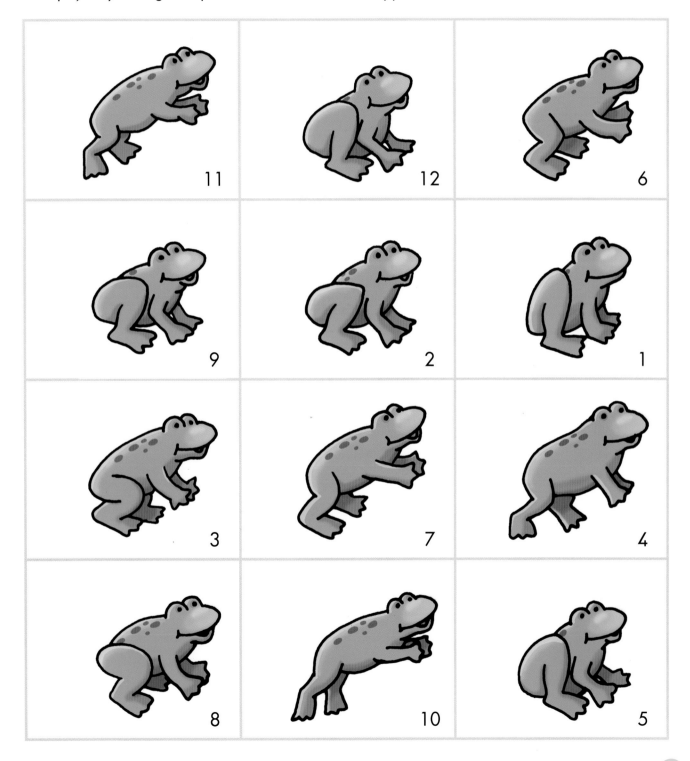

11

12

6

9

2

1

3

7

4

8

10

5

My Counting Mini Book

☼ Cut along the <u>solid</u> lines.

☼ Fold on the <u>dotted</u> lines and staple.

☼ Count the pictures in each box and write how many.

I'll count the bugs.

☐ bugs

4

I'll count the mugs.

☐ mugs

5

I'll count the cats.
I'll count the hats.

☐ hats ☐ cats

8

_____'s

Counting
Book

1 6 3 9 2

1

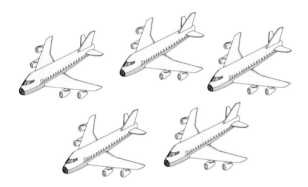

I'll count the jets.

☐ jets

6

I'll count the frogs.

☐ frogs

3

I'll count the dogs.

☐ dogs

2

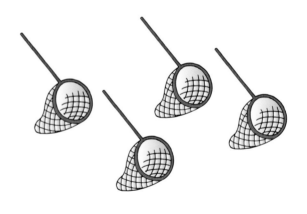

I'll count the nets.

☐ nets

7

My Piggy Bank Mini Book

○ Cut along the <u>solid</u> lines.

○ Fold on the <u>dotted</u> lines and staple.

○ Write number words **zero**, **six**, **seven**, **eight**, **nine**, and **ten** to finish the book.

I have _____ pennies.

4

I have _____ pennies.

5

I have _____ pennies.

8

_____

1

I have _____
pennies.

6

I have _____
pennies.

3

zero	• •	7
six	• •	9
seven	• •	0
eight	• •	8
nine	• •	10
ten	• •	6

2

I have _____
pennies.

7

MATH+ Step In • Gr. PreK–K © 2011 Creative Teaching Press

Finish Line Game

❶ Cut out the number cards. Shuffle them into a pile.

❷ Each player takes a card from the pile and writes his or her number in the first box. The player with the bigger number circles that box.

❸ Play continues until all the boxes are filled. The player with the most circled boxes wins.

MATERIALS
- ✓ number fact cards (pages 111-114)
- ✓ pencils

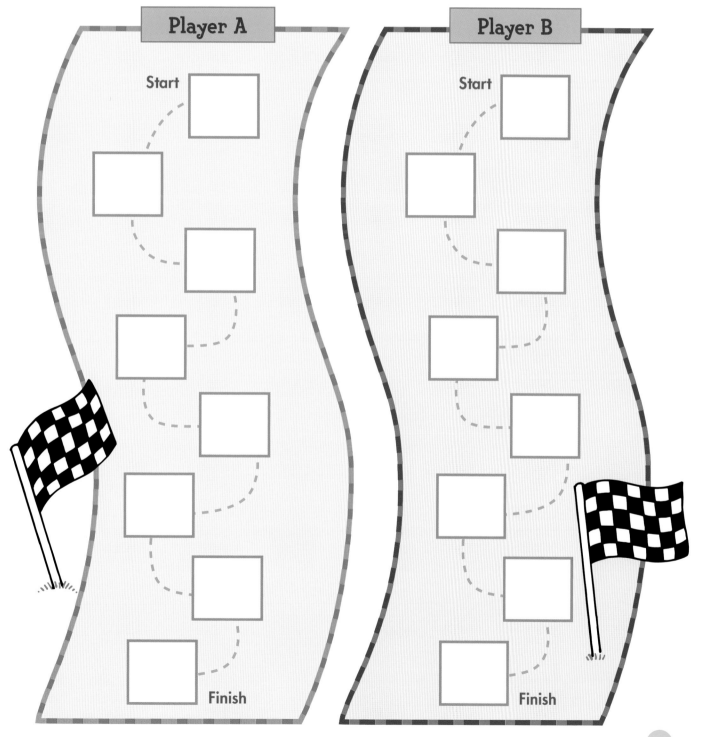

Player A

Start

Finish

Player B

Start

Finish

Shapes Blackout Game

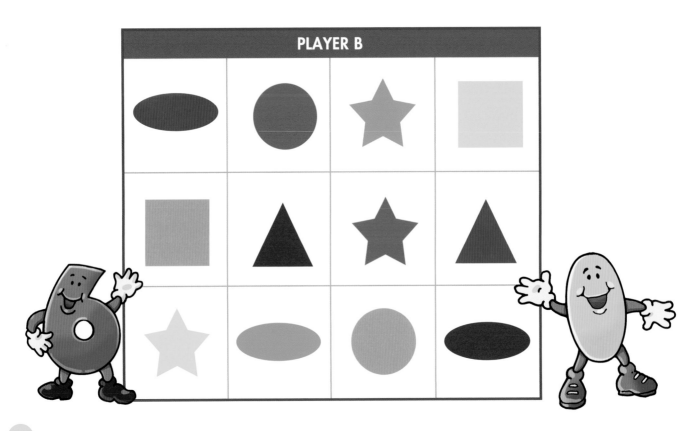

MATH+ Step In • Gr. PreK–K © 2011 Creative Teaching Press

Shapes Blackout Game

HOW TO PLAY

① Cut out the shape boxes below. Put them facedown in a pile.

② The first player draws a card and says its color and shape out loud. Whoever has that colored shape on his or her game board, covers it with a marker.

③ Players take turns until all the colored shapes on one player's game board are completely covered.

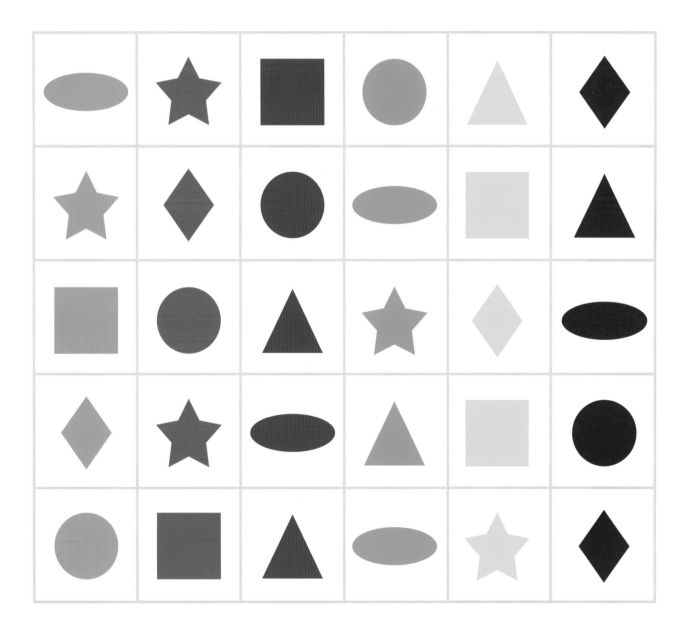

See Them Run! Mini Book

⚙ Write your name on the first page.

⚙ Cut along the <u>solid</u> lines and staple.

⚙ Read your book.

See Them Run!

 by

_____

\- \- \- \- \- \- \- \- \- \- \- \- \- \-

_____

1

A cat ran under a fence.

2

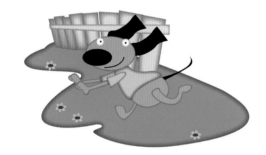

A dog ran around the fence.

3

A mouse ran in front of a tree.

4

A bear ran behind the tree.

5

They all met for lunch.
Yum, yum!

6

MATH Fact Cards

Tips for Using MATH Fact Cards

Before cutting the fact cards apart, consider laminating them in order to use them with a dry-erase marker. Laminating the cards also makes them more durable. Punching a hole in the upper left-hand corner of each card and storing the cards on a ring is also a good way to keep the cards organized and easy to use.

Here are some suggestions for using the fact cards:

- Use a timer to see how quickly each math fact is recognized. Begin with a small number of cards. Add more cards once your child achieves increased speed and confidence.

- Challenge your child to expand the fact card information. For example, ask your child to name two fruits that are red, or to give examples of other things that are tall, heavy, or closed.

- Have your child match the color words on page 108 to their corresponding colored shapes on page 109.

- Play a sorting game. Shuffle the number fact cards on pages 111 and 113 and have your child sort them into groups of even and odd numbers. Another option is to have your child sort the cards into groups of 1–10 and 11–20.

- Extend the concept of math-related opposites with your child. For example, have him or her provide the opposite for words such as *true, inside, top, before, together,* and *none (false, outside, bottom, after, apart, all).*

- Extend the concept of day and night with your child. Have him or her list (or draw) three things that typically happen during the day and three things that typically happen at night. For a more sophisticated alternate, have your child identify things that typically happen during the morning, the afternoon, the evening, and at night.

- Extend the concept of shapes with your child. Have your child look around your house for objects that are shaped like circles, squares, triangles, and rectangles.

Color Fact Cards

Color Fact Cards

red	orange
yellow	green
blue	purple
pink	brown
black	white

MATH+ Step In • Gr. PreK–K © 2011 Creative Teaching Press

Shape and Pattern Fact Cards

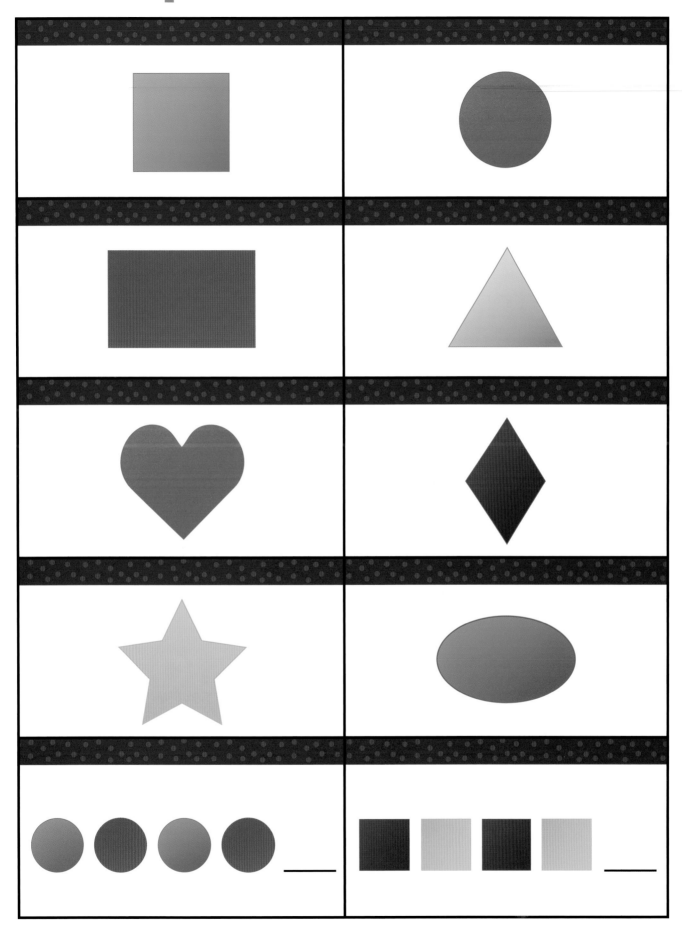

Shape and Pattern Fact Cards

circle	square
triangle	**rectangle**
diamond	**heart**
oval	**star**

MATH+ Step In • Gr. PreK–K © 2011 Creative Teaching Press

Number Fact Cards

1

2

3

4

5

6

7

8

9

10

Number Fact Cards

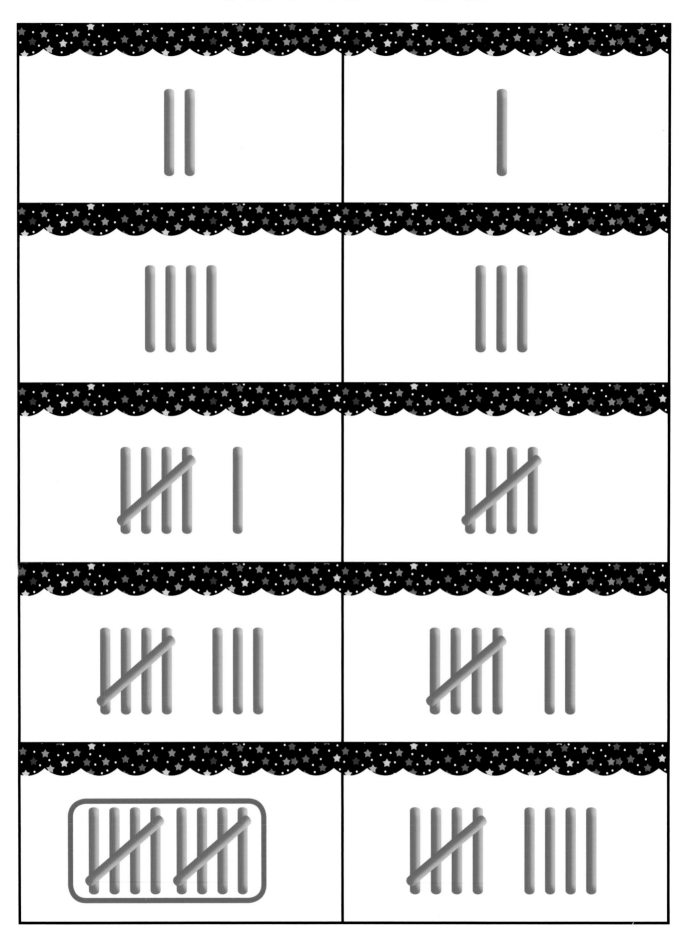

Number Fact Cards

11	12
13	14
15	16
17	18
19	20

Number Fact Cards

Number and Time Fact Cards

10	20	___	40	50
60	70	80	90	100

10	20	30	___	50
60	70	80	90	100

10	20	30	40	___
60	70	80	90	100

10	20	30	40	50
___	70	80	90	100

10	20	30	40	50
60	___	80	90	100

10	20	30	40	50
60	70	___	90	100

10	20	30	40	50
60	70	80	___	100

10	20	30	40	50
60	70	80	90	___

day

night

Number and Time Fact Cards

40	30
60	50
80	70
100	90

MATH+ Step In • Gr. PreK–K © 2011 Creative Teaching Press

Money and Opposites Fact Cards

nickel

penny

quarter

dime

heavy →

long

first

← near

open

full →

Money and Opposites Fact Cards

1¢ or 1 cent	5¢ or 5 cents = 5 pennies
10¢ or 10 cents = 10 pennies	25¢ or 25 cents = 25 pennies

short

← light

far away →

↑ last

← empty

↑ closed

MATH+ Step In • Gr. PreK–K © 2011 Creative Teaching Press

Answer Key

PAGE 7

PAGE 8

PAGE 9

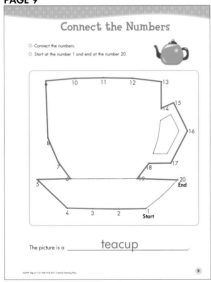

PAGE 10

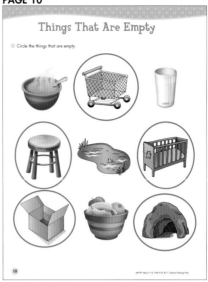

PAGE 11

1. tent
2. cent
3. net
4. note
5. planet

PAGE 12

PAGE 13

Hidden Picture

- Follow the directions to see what is hiding.
- Write your answer below.

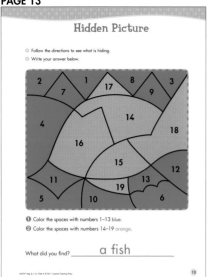

❶ Color the spaces with numbers 1–13 blue.
❷ Color the spaces with numbers 14–19 orange.

What did you find? _____a fish_____

13

PAGE 14

An Odd Snowman

- Use the key to color the snowman.

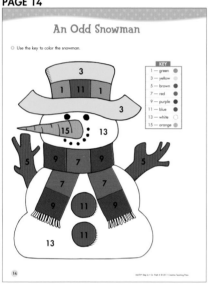

KEY
1 — green
3 — yellow
5 — brown
7 — red
9 — purple
11 — blue
13 — white
15 — orange

14

PAGE 15

Hidden Numbers

- Circle the hidden numbers.
- Then write how many you found.

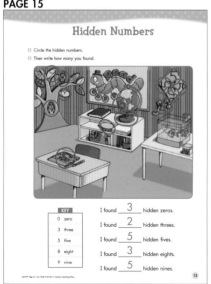

KEY
0 zero
3 three
5 five
8 eight
9 nine

I found ___3___ hidden zeros.
I found ___2___ hidden threes.
I found ___5___ hidden fives.
I found ___3___ hidden eights.
I found ___5___ hidden nines.

15

PAGE 16

Go Fish 1–25

- Connect the dots.
- Color the picture.

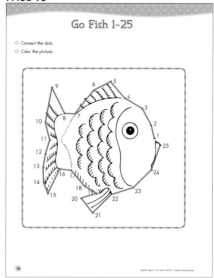

16

PAGE 17

The Beehive Maze

- Circle the odd numbers to help the bee get to the hive.

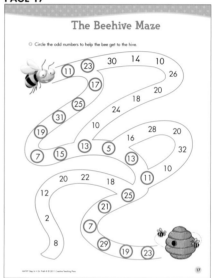

17

PAGE 18

The Hidden Path

- Color the triangles to help the gingerbread man find his way home.

18

120

PAGE 19

A. 2s; a pig
B. 5s; a barn

PAGE 20

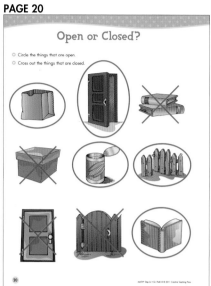

PAGE 21

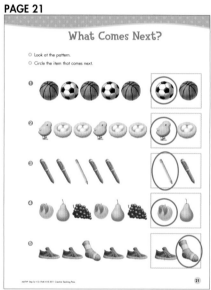

PAGE 22

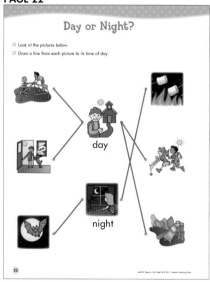

PAGE 23

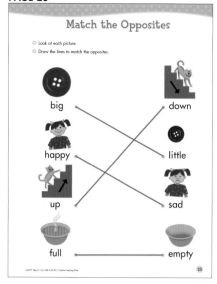

PAGE 24

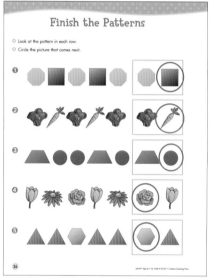

PAGE 25

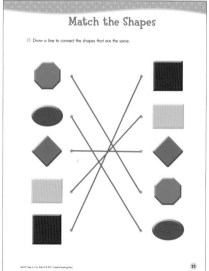

PAGE 26

three horses
six chickens
five pigs
two cows

PAGE 27

1. last, first, next
2. first, last, next
3. first, next, last

PAGE 28

PAGE 29

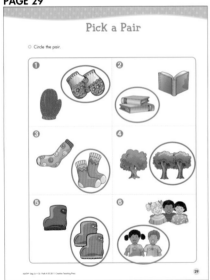

PAGE 30

PAGE 31

PAGE 32

PAGE 33

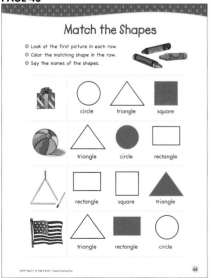

PAGE 35
14

PAGE 36
Possible answers: Same colors; 3-sided

PAGE 37
13

PAGE 38
3

PAGE 39
14

PAGE 40
4

PAGE 41
3

PAGE 42
Possible answers: Heart, circle, star

PAGE 43

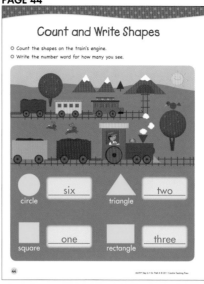

PAGE 44

PAGE 45
A book

PAGE 46
Over

PAGE 47
After

PAGE 48
A branch

PAGE 49
The tree trunk

PAGE 50
Possible answer: It was too big.

PAGE 51
Over

PAGE 52
The bear

PAGE 54

PAGE 55
Possible answers: Eyes, eyelashes, eyebrows, eyeballs

PAGE 56
Two

PAGE 57
Three

PAGE 58
1 more

PAGE 59
Five

PAGE 60
Six

PAGE 61
21

PAGE 62
A tail

PAGE 63

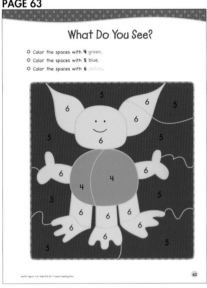

PAGE 65
They both have spots (or dots).

PAGE 66
1, 3, 5

PAGE 67
5

PAGE 68
5

PAGE 69
8

PAGE 70
2, 4, 6

PAGE 71
2 pairs—a gray pair and an orange pair

PAGE 72
1 more

PAGE 73
Possible answers: A pair of eyes; a pair of ears; a pair of feet

PAGE 74
4

PAGE 75
18

PAGE 76
3

PAGE 77
14

PAGE 78
2, 4, 6, 8

PAGE 79
4

PAGE 80
20

PAGE 81

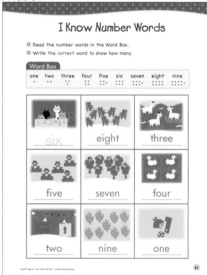

PAGE 82

PAGE 83
Possible answers: A pair of tires (or wheels); a pair of pedals

PAGE 84
The baseball

PAGE 85
Possible answers: They both are animals, have a tail, have 2 ears, wear clothes, etc.

PAGE 86
Possible answers: Fish food; fish tank; the things in the fish tank

PAGE 87
The vase

PAGE 88
Possible answers: Leaves, branches, tree trunk

PAGE 89
Possible answers: 2 trees; 2 mushrooms; 2 rocks; 2 friends; 2 shoes; 2 hands (or paws)

PAGE 90
Answers will vary.

PAGE 91

PAGE 92

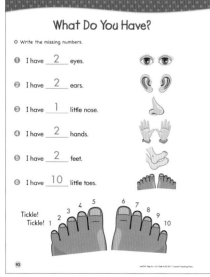

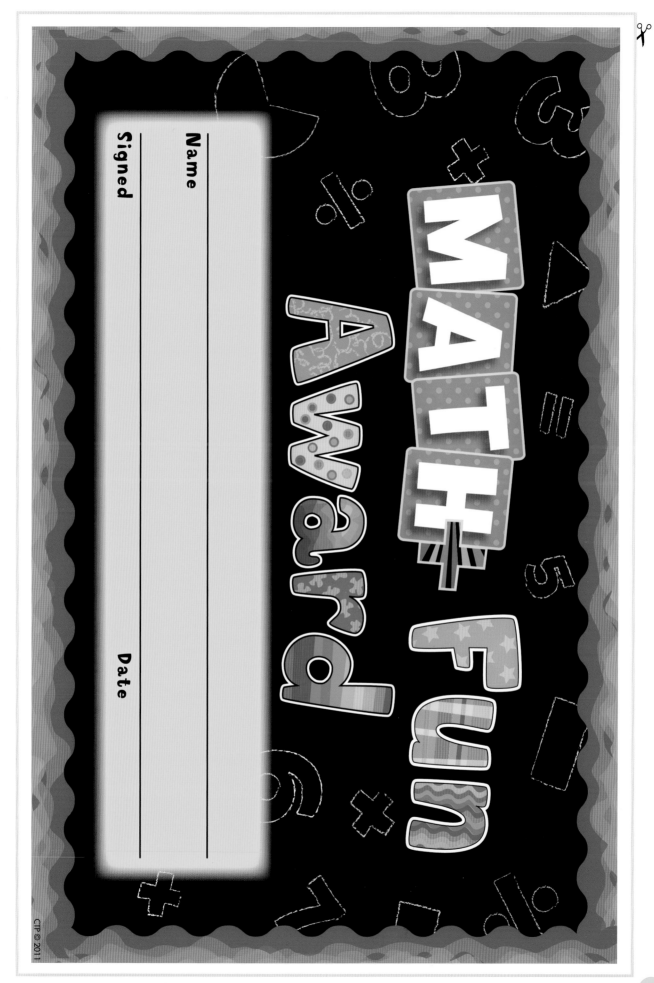

MATH Fun Award

Name

Signed

Date